Pokémon ADVENTURES
HeartGold & SoulSilver
Volume 2
Perfect Square Edition

Story by **HIDENORI KUSAKA**
Art by **SATOSHI YAMAMOTO**

© 2013 The Pokémon Company International.
© 1995–2013 Nintendo/Creatures Inc./GAME FREAK inc.
TM, ®, and character names are trademarks of Nintendo.
POCKET MONSTERS SPECIAL Vol. 42 and Vol. 43
by Hidenori KUSAKA, Satoshi YAMAMOTO
© 1997 Hidenori KUSAKA, Satoshi YAMAMOTO
All rights reserved.
Original Japanese edition published by SHOGAKUKAN.
English translation rights in the United States of America,
Canada, the United Kingdom, Ireland, Australia, New Zealand
and India arranged with SHOGAKUKAN.

English Adaptation/Bryant Turnage
Translation/Tetsuichiro Miyaki
Touch-up & Lettering/Annaliese Christman
Design/Shawn Carrico
Editor/Annette Roman

Printed in the U.S.A.

Published by VIZ Media, LLC
P.O. Box 77010
San Francisco, CA 94107

10 9 8 7
First printing, November 2013
Seventh printing, September 2018

www.perfectsquare.com   www.viz.com

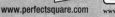

...TURES

SOULSILVER

OUR STORY TAKES PLACE IN THE JOHTO REGION, SEVERAL YEARS AFTER THE NOTORIOUS INCIDENT WITH THE MASKED MAN. TEAM ROCKET HAS MADE A COMEBACK AND ARE PURSUING THE MYSTERIOUS POKÉMON ARCEUS. AFTER WINNING THE POKÉATHLON, GOLD HEADS DOWN TO ECRUTEAK CITY IN SEARCH OF DRAGON-TYPE TRAINER LANCE, WHO HAS INFORMATION ABOUT ARCEUS. MEANWHILE, SILVER, WHO IS ALSO IN PURSUIT OF TEAM ROCKET, IS ATTACKED IN THE SAFARI ZONE BY PETREL, ONE OF THE FOUR TEAM ROCKET EXECUTIVES.

BOYS AND GIRLS AND THEIR POKÉMON... YOUNG PEOPLE, DETERMINED TO WIN, SENT OUT INTO THE WORLD WITH A POKÉDEX BY THEIR MENTORS AND PROFESSORS ...

JOHTO REGION

Sinjoh Ruins ?

Gold

AN UNCOUTH BUT PASSIONATE POKÉMON TRAINER ALSO KNOWN AS THE HATCHER. A CAREFREE SOUL WHO OFTEN PUSHES HIS LUCK, YET IS UNABLE TO IGNORE THE PLIGHT OF PEOPLE AND POKÉMON IN TROUBLE.

HEART GOL

SILVER IS REU
WITH CRYSTA
TOGETHER T
FOR ECRUTEA
BUT ON THE W
COME FACE T
WITH ARIANA,
MEMBER OF
ROCKET EXEC

A POKÉMON SPECIALIST KN
THE CATCHER WHO TEACHI
THE POKÉMON ACADEMY.
TO JOIN SILVER ON HIS QUE
PROTECT THE FUTURE FOR
STUDENTS FROM THE SCH
TEAM ROCKET

Locations in this v

Ecru

Route 38

Rui

Silver

ALSO KNOWN AS
THE EXCHANGER. HE
HAS A DARK PAST,
BUT HAS OVERCOME
IT AND IS READY TO
EMBRACE HIS
DESTINY.

ARCHER

THIS FANATICAL FOLLOWER OF GIOVANNI IS THE LEADER OF THE TEAM ROCKET EXECUTIVES WHO CONTROL THE NEW TEAM ROCKET. ARCHER IS SEARCHING FOR ARCEUS.

PROTON

THIS TEAM ROCKET EXECUTIVE, WHO EXCELS IN LOGICAL THINKING AND ANALYSIS, IS IN CHARGE OF LOCATING THE SINJOH RUINS. A CALM MAN DEVOTED TO HIS WORK.

PETREL

THIS TEAM ROCKET EXECUTIVE IS A MASTER OF DISGUISE. HE USES HIS SKILL TO SNEAK INTO VARIOUS LOCATIONS AND SEARCH FOR SIXTEEN MYSTERIOUS PLATES.

ARIANA

THE ONLY FEMALE MEMBER OF THE TEAM ROCKET EXECUTIVES IS IN CHARGE OF ELIMINATING ANYTHING THAT MIGHT STAND IN THE WAY OF TEAM ROCKET'S GOALS. SHE ATTACKED SILVER AND CRYS WITH HER POWERFULLY TRAINED POKÉMON.

THE GYM LEADER OF ECRUTEAK CITY. NICKNAMED THE "MYSTIC SEER OF THE FUTURE" DUE TO HIS ABILITY TO SEARCH FOR MISSING PEOPLE AND OBJECTS. FRIENDS WITH EUSINE.

THE GYM LEADER OF VIOLET CITY. KNOWN AS THE "ELEGANT MASTER OF FLYING POKÉMON," HE FOLLOWED IN HIS FATHER WALKER'S FOOTSTEPS TO BECOME A GYM LEADER.

THE GYM LEADER OF AZALEA GYM. KNOWN AS THE "WALKING BUG POKÉMON ENCYCLOPEDIA," HE HAS COPIOUS KNOWLEDGE OF BUG-TYPE POKÉMON. HIS TRADEMARK IS HIS BUTTERFLY NET.

THE GYM LEADER OF CIANWOOD CITY. KNOWN AS "HIS ROARING FISTS DO THE TALKING," HE IS A FAMOUS MARTIAL ARTIST WHO RUNS HIS OWN MARTIAL ARTS DOJO. HE IS ALSO BLUE'S MARTIAL ARTS MASTER.

LANCE

A TRAINER WHO SPECIALIZES IN DRAGON-TYPE POKÉMON AND THE FORMER LEADER OF THE KANTO ELITE FOUR. POSSESSES IMPORTANT INFORMATION ABOUT ARCEUS, BUT HAS MYSTERIOUSLY DISAPPEARED.

POKÉMON

ADVENTURES
HEARTGOLD & SOULSILVER

CONTENTS

FORGIVE ME, CRYS...

AS A MATTER OF FACT... IT'S **TOO** POWERFUL.

JUST AS I THOUGH... IT'S SUPER POWER FUL NOW

I HAVE NO CHOICE BUT TO LET YOU FINISH THIS BATTLE WHILE I GO ON TO ECRUTEAK CITY... ALONE!!

NOW THAT I KNOW HOW DANGEROUS THEY ARE...

ECR TEA CIT GYI ...

WHAT BRINGS YOU TO THIS GYM?

I'M HERE TO SEE MORTY, THE GYM LEADER.

...

"...ANOTHER ONE"?

ANOTHER ONE, FALKNER.

ANOTH[ER] ONE [,] BUGS[Y.]

THAT'S RIGHT.

MORTY'S HAD SEVERAL VISITORS OVER THE PAST FEW DAYS...

...WHO ASKED HIM TO LOOK INTO THE FUTURE FOR THEM.

17

CAN YOU TELL US ABOUT THAT POKÉMON OF YOURS?

DO YOU KNOW THIS POKÉMON?

HOLD ON, CHUCK. THIS IS...

WHA... WRO... HITM... TO...

IT WAS GIVEN TO ME BY BLUE, THE GYM LEADER OF VIRIDIAN CITY.

THIS RHYPE... IO...

...THE EVOLVED FORM OF RHYDON.

HITMON-TOP HAS FOUGHT RHYDON BEFORE.

OH! I SEE NOW!

WHA... BY BLUE...

21

NO ONE'S HERE... NOT GIOVANNI... OR URSARING...

WHERE HAVE THEY GONE...?

IT'S NO SURPRISE. IT'S BEEN THREE MONTHS...

I THINK I'VE MANAGED TO DECIPHER IT.

...THAT BOOK YOU ASKED ME ABOUT...

Secrets of the Land

HUH?

BLUE, I'M SO GRATEFU TO YOU FOR COMING WITH ME TODAY. THIS ISN' MUCH, BUT...

I SEE.

FALKNER, BUGSY... YOU DON'T HAVE ANY OBJECTION, DO YOU?

YOU MAY GO SEE MORTY.

WELL, IF BLUE RECOGNIZES YOU AS A SKILLED TRAINER, I SEE NO REASON TO TURN YOU AWAY.

FSSST

IT'S ...RK IN ...ERE, SO ...TCH ...UR ...TEP.

NOPE.

I'LL TAKE YOU TO HIM.

...E'S A ...SY ...JY!

SOMEONE... ELSE?

YOU'LL HAVE TO WAIT UNTIL THEY'RE DONE.

MORTY IS MEETING WITH SOMEONE ELSE AT THE MOMENT THOUGH.

28

38

39

B-BMP

BUT...

...IF WHAT ARCHER JUST SAID IS TRUE...

BUT THIS ONE IS UNLIKE ANY OF THEM! THERE'S SOMETHING SO INTENSE ABOUT IT...

I'VE MET ALL SORTS OF POKÉMON.

I'VE NEVE FELT ANYTHI LIKE THI BEFOR...

B-BMP

...DOESN'T BELONG TO ANYONE— YET!!

...THEN THIS POKÉMON...

◉ Megaree/Meganium ♂ `GRASS`

- Lv. 80 (As of Adv. 450)
- Ability: Overgrow
- Hardy Nature. Good Endurance.

A gutsy Pokémon with special grass-type moves.

◉ Bonee/Cubone ♂ `GROUND`

- Lv. 73 (As of Adv. 450)
- Ability: Lightningrod
- Lonely Nature. Persistent.

Fights with its bone in both close combat and long range battles.

◉ Parasee/Parasect ♀ `BUG` `GRASS`

- Lv. 75 (As of Adv. 450)
- Ability: Dry Skin
- Brave Nature. Often dozes off.

Creates medicines by blending its spores.

◉ Monlee/Hitmonchan ♂ `FIGHTING`

- Lv. 78 (As of Adv. 450)
- Ability: Iron Fist
- Adamant Nature. Strong willed.

A powerful fighter with various punch attacks.

◉ Archy/Arcanine ♂ `FIRE`

- Lv. 79 (As of Adv. 450)
- Ability: Intimidate
- Hasty Nature. Loves to run.

Runs swiftly with Crys mounted on its back. Powerful Fire-type moves.

◉ Natee/Xatu ♀ `PSYCHIC` `FLYING`

- Lv. 60 (As of Adv.450)
- Ability: Early Bird
- Quiet Nature. Somewhat vain

Lifts Crys up in aerial battles.

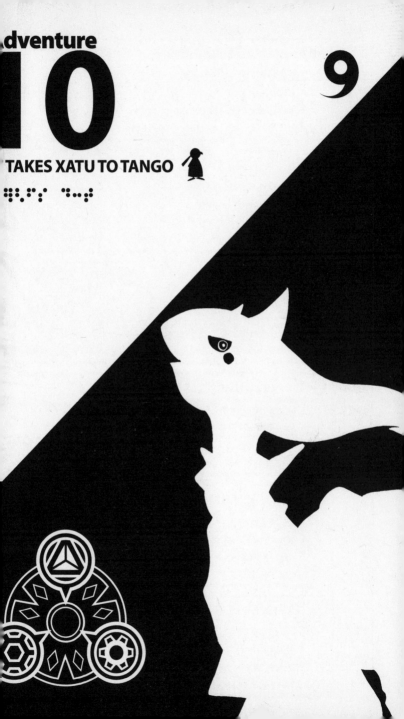

THAT'S [LOGICAL] AND [UNDER]STANDABLE.

SINCE THIS POKÉMON IS COMPLETELY UNKNOWN TO HER, SHE'S USING THAT BALL TO ASSESS ITS STRENGTH BEFORE FORMULATING A PLAN TO CAPTURE IT...

A LEVEL BALL... CLEVER!

...THE INCREDIBLE ALPHA POKÉMON ARCEUS. WE'VE BEEN TRYING TO GET OUR HANDS ON IT FOR THE LONGEST TIME.

BUT IT'S RATHER A SURPRISE THAT SHE DECIDED TO ATTEMPT TO CAPTURE...

SO I'LL USE...

THE LEVEL BALL DIDN'T WORK.

SHOULDN'T WE DO SOMETHING, ARCHER?!

...

JUST WATCH, ARIANA.

48

...SO IT LEADS HER INTO THE SINJOH RUINS.

...IS FOR HER TO OPEN ARCEUS'S HEART...

..AND I'M HAPPY O LET HIM.

HE'S TRYING TO GATHER THE PLATES BEFORE WE DO...

THAT RED-HAIRED KID...

I CHANGED MY PLAN AFTER ARCHER UPDATED ME.

THE SAME GOES FOR THE PLATES.

..ALL **WE** HAVE TO DO IS **STEAL** THEM FROM HIM!

ONCE HE DOES THE WORK OF GATHERING ALL SIXTEEN PLATES...

NOW **THAT** PLAN, I **LIKE!**

HA HA HA HA!

HA...

...WE JUST NEED TO SIT AND WAIT?

SO, MOSTLY...

ECRU-
TEAK
CITY
GYM...

SILVER,
OLD
BUDDY,
?!

WHAT A
COINCI-
DENCE!
WHAT'S
UP...

HEY!!

SHOW YOUR-SELF!!

WHO ATTACKED ME?!

Adventure

11

9

ALL ABOUT ARCEUS I

IT'S ALL RIGHT. I'M FINE.

ANOTHER IMAGE CAME INTO MY HEAD... RIGHT BEFORE THE LOCATIONS OF THE THIRTEEN PLATES...

IT WAS AN IMAGE OF...

...THAT HUGE SHADOW... THAT ATTACKED THE GYM.

HEY!!

THEY WERE GOING TO **COMBINE** THEM...!

AND THE MYSTIC PROPERTIES OF PLATES THAT CAN BOOST THE POWER OF A POKÉMON'S MOVES...

A POKÉMON POWERFUL ENOUGH TO INFLICT SUCH DAMAGE...

THERE WERE THIRTEEN AREAS OF ENERGY... SCATTERED AROUND JOHTO...

LIKE YOU SAID...

HERE YOU GO, SILVER...

MAYBE THOSE PEOPLE W... WERE HER... THESE LAS... FEW DAY... CAME FO... THE SAM... REASON...

VISUALIZING THE LOCATIONS OF THESE THIRTEEN DIFFERENT PLACES... WAS...

I'VE MARKED THE LOCA-TIONS ON THIS MAP...

"WE NEED YOUR HELP."

...FOR THE OTHER WEAVILES. THEY READ, "WE'RE LOOKING FOR SQUARE OBJECTS KNOWN AS PLATES.

WE'VE BEE LEAVING MESSAGE ON THE ROUTES A TOWNS W TRAVELE TO AND I THE SAFA ZONE...

...SPREADS THROUGH- OUT THE REGION.

THAT'S HOW OUR MES- SAGE...

...COPY THEM ONTO TREES IN THEIR TERRITORY.

THE SNEASE AND WEAVIL THAT S OUR MESSA

AND THAT'S HOW...

IT KEE TRAVE EVE AS SPEA

OH MY ...!

...WE'VE SURVIVED ALL THIS TIME.

... AVERT DISASTER!!

PLEASE HELP US TO...

BUT IT'S CLEAR THAT A CRISIS IS HEADING TOWARDS JOHTO...

WE DON HAV AN MO HEL TO G YOU

THE THREE SIMPLE SECRETS— REPORT, COMMUNI- CATE AND CONSULT... HM...

HEH ...

ALREADY REGIS- TERED ...

I WAS RIGHT!

TAL OLD OAK ELM GREEN BLUE

POKEM POKEM

AND IF I KNOW HER LIKE I THINK I DO...

CR MA SUR TO TH POK GE WI ME

Adventure
12
9

ALL ABOUT ARCEUS II

82

84

I'M PUSHING AND HITTING THIS THING BUT NOTHING'S HAPPENING!!

NUTS!!

ISN'T THERE ANY WAY AROUND THIS...?!

HAVE YOU EVER BEEN TO THE MUSEUM IN THE BASEMENT OF THE POKÉATHLON DOME?

ARCEUS HAS CAPTURED GOLD INSIDE THAT SPHERE!

YOU CAN READ ABOUT THE ORIGIN OF THE POKÉ-ATHLON THERE.

...

THERE WAS A DEADLY PANDEMIC.

A LONG TIME AGO ON AN ISLAND IN A FAR-OFF REGION...

100

...BEFORE THEY COULD REACH THE LEGENDARY POKÉMON.

THEY WERE FACED WITH TEN ORDEALS...

...SET OUT ON A JOURNEY TO MEET A LEGENDARY POKÉMON WHO IT WAS SAID COULD CURE THIS PLAGUE.

ONE PERSON AND THE GROUP POKÉMO...

THESE WERE CHALLENGES THAT COULD ONLY BE OVERCOME BY MUSTERING ALL THEIR COURAGE AND WORKING **TOGETHER**.

THOSE ORDEALS COULD NOT BE COMPLETED BY JUST PEOPLE POKÉMON ALONE.

...THE POKÉATHLON ORIGINATED.

AND THAT'S HOW...

THAT PERSON AND THEIR POKÉMON WENT DOWN IN HISTORY AS HEROES.

IN THE END THEY MASTERED THE TRIAL AND RECEIVED THE CURE FOR THE PLAGUE FROM THE LEGENDARY POKÉMON.

...THE ISLANDERS CREATED TEN SPORTS TO REPLICATE THOSE TEN ORDEALS.

TO HONOR THIS STORY AND PASS IT DOWN TO NEXT GENERATIONS...

...TO SEE PEOPLE AND POKÉMON WORKING TOGETHER LIKE THAT HERO OF LEGEND AND...

I CHOSE THE POKÉATHLON DOME AS OUR MEETING PLACE IN HOPES THAT IT WOULD ASSUAGE ARCEUS'S GRIEF...

HEH... I'M A LOT MORE INTERESTED IN THAT POKÉMON THAN THIS ONE—ARCEUS IS A TERROR!

...THE LEGENDARY POKÉMON WHO CURED THE PLAGUE.

...I HAVE NO CHOICE BUT TO GO THERE IN PERSON...

IT APPEARS...

I'D LOVE TO FIND OUT WHAT KIND OF POKÉMON IT WAS...

venture

3

9

ABOUT ARCEUS III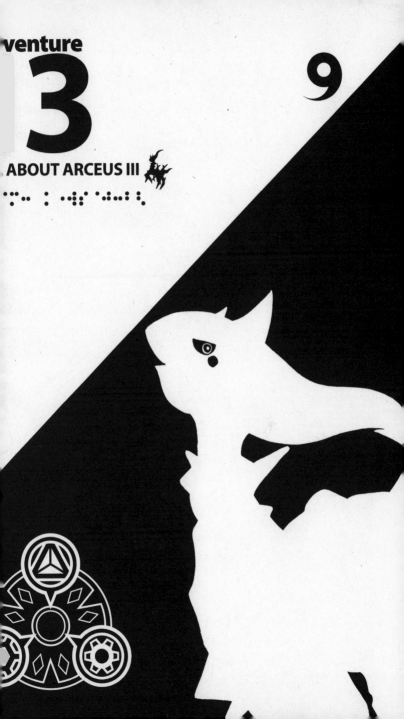

⠁⠃⠕⠥⠞⠀⠒⠀⠁⠗⠉⠑⠥⠎⠒

THIS INFORMATION SPREAD LIKE WILDFIRE THROUGH THE JOHTO REGION VIA THE CLAW MARKS LEFT ON TREES BY THE WEAVILE.

MORTY MANAGED TO PINPOINT THE WHEREABOUTS OF THE PLATES!

...AND PROCURED THEM.

S.S. AQUA

SILVER QUICKLY TRAVELED TO THE LOCATION OF EACH PLATE...

FINALLY...

I'VE DONE IT!

ME TEEN ATES

110

RMBL RMBL

SICALLY, IT'S LIKE A PORTAL TO ANOTHER WORLD.

THAT SPHERE EXISTS IN BOTH THE RUINS OF ALPH AND ANOTHER REALM...

ARCEUS HAS CREATED A POWERFUL SPHERE AROUND ITSELF.

THE ENTRANCE TO THE SINJOH RUINS...

A PORTAL...

RMBL

112

IT WAS THESE...

...MY POCKET HEAT UP WHEN WE ENTERED THE SPHERE...

OH!

...I FELT SOMETHING **CHANGE** ABOUT ARCEUS... RIGHT WHEN YOU JUMPED INSIDE THIS BOUNCY SPHERE WITH US.

AN IT M JUST MY IM NAT BU

HM! AND I FELT...

IT SEEM LIKE AL A SUD ARCE DIDN'T TO CON ITS ATT

ACK!

A PLACE NEITHER SINNOH NOR JOHTO... **THAT** IS THE SINJOH RUINS.

WE'RE IN THE SINJOH RUINS. AND THEY LOOK A LOT LIKE THE PLACE WHERE WE AWAKENED ARCEUS IN THE SINNOH REGION.

THERE IS A THEORY THAT A GROUP OF PEOPLE FROM SINNOH EMIGRATED TO JOHTO, WHERE THE CULTURES OF THOSE TWO REGIONS FUSED TOGETHER.

WH, AR **YO** DO HER

ARCEUS!!

...THAT IT OPENED ITS HEART AND LED US TO THE SINJOH RUINS.

IT'S BECAUSE YOU THREE GENUINELY TRIED TO COMMUNICATE WITH ARCEUS...

I'M QUITE GRATEFUL TO YOU.

YANK

NO WONDER I COULDN'T FIND THEM!

I NEVER DREAMED THEY WOULD BE LOCATED IN ANOTHER WORLD!

HAND THEM OVER!

YOU'VE GATHERED ALL THE PLATES FOR US TOO. HOW KIND OF YOU. NOW...

THANK YOU EVER SO MUCH.

⊙ Feraligatr/Feraligatr ♂ `WATER`

- Lv. 83 (As of Adventure 454)
- Ability: Torrent
- Quiet Nature. Thoroughly Cunning.

Helps Silver travel over water and has mastered special water-type moves.

⊙ Weavile/Weavile ♂ `DARK` `ICE`

- Lv. 84 (As of Adventure 454)
- Ability: Pressure
- Quirky Nature. Likes to fight.

Has been with Silver for a long time. A swift fighter.

⊙ Kingdra/Kingdra ♀ `WATER` `DRAGON`

- Lv. 80 (As of Adventure 454)
- Ability: Swift Swim
- Serious Nature. Often dozes off.

Evolved when traded with Gold. A powerful attacker.

⊙ Honchkrow/Honchkrow♂ `DARK` `FLYING`

- Lv. 79 (As of Adventure 454)
- Ability: Insomnia
- Adamant Nature. Quick tempered.

Helps Silver fly and attacks well in the dark.

⊙ Gyarados/Gyarados ♂ `WATER` `FLYING`

- Lv. 80 (As of Adventure 454)
- Ability: Intimidate
- Sassy Nature. Often thrashes about.

A red Gyarados who Silver captured at the Lake of Rage.

⊙ Rhyperior/Rhyperior ♂ `GROUND` `ROCK`

- Lv. 81 (As of Adventure 454)
- Ability: Lightningrod
- Mild Nature. Proud of its power.

Blue's Rhydon evolved with the power of the Protector.

venture
14

9

ABOUT ARCEUS IV

⠁⠃⠕⠥⠞ ⠁⠗⠉⠑⠥⠎

AS LONG AS I HAVE THESE PLATES, ARCEUS'S VAST POWER IS UNDER MY COMMAND!

I DON'T KNOW WHAT HAPPENED EXACTLY...

BUT ONE DAY THAT RELATIONSHIP WAS BROKEN.

ARC

...I HEAR THERE ONCE WAS A TIME WHEN YOU LIVED TOGETHER WITH PEOPLE IN HARMONY.

...LOCKED IT INTO THESE PLATES SO THAT THEY COULD WIELD YOUR AWESOME POWER.

...BUT SOME PEOPLE STOLE YOUR ABILITY TO SHIFT YOUR TYPE AND...

SO I COULD ACQUIRE YOUR POWER!!

THE CHANGE IN YOUR RELATIONSHIP WITH PEOPLE... YOUR LOSS OF POWER... I SUPPOSE YOU HAD NO CHOICE BUT TO DROWN YOUR SORROW BY SLIPPING INTO AN EVERLASTING SLUMBER.

WHICH IS WHY I LURED YOU DOWN HERE AGAIN!

WHAT A WASTE. TRULY A WASTE.

GIVE THE PLATES TO THEM!

SO WHY DID YOU...

MY HUNCH WAS RIGHT!

I KNEW IT...!

134

IDIOTS!!

DUNNO.

UHHH...

YOU TOO GOLD WHY D YOU TE HIM T HAN THE OVER

THERE WASN'T ANY OPPORTUNITY TO BARGAIN WITH THEM.

SEEMED LIKE THE BE COURSE C ACTION A THE TIME

THE PLATES BELONG TO THOSE WHO CAN MAKE THE BEST USE OF THEM.

AHAHAHA! A WISE DECISION.

AFTER AL THEY'RE HOLDING ARCEUS HOSTAGE

OF COURSE!

...

135

FLAME PLATE!!
SPLASH PLATE!!
MEADOW PLATE!!
ZAP PLATE!!
ICICLE PLATE!!
FIST PLATE!!
TOXIC PLATE!!
EARTH PLATE!!

...THE OH RUINS U HADN'T NE SO OMPANIED ARCEUS.

WE COULDN'T HAVE ENTERED ...

YOU HELPED US ACHIEVE OUR AIM TOO, YOU KNOW.

WHAT ?!

LITTLE GIRL...

THE ONE WITH THE GREATEST DESIRE TO POSSESS ARCEUS'S POWER IS THE RIGHTFUL OWNER OF THESE SIXTEEN PLATES!!

SKY PLATE!!
MIND PLATE!!
INSECT PLATE!!
STONE PLATE!!
SPOOKY PLATE!!
DRACO PLATE!!
DREAD PLATE!!
IRON PLATE!!

THAT BATTLE OPENED UP ITS HEART, WHICH HERETO-FORE WAS FILLED WITH HATRED.

ALTHOUGH IT WAS ONLY A SHORT BATTLE, SOMETHING ABOUT IT MUST HAVE STRUCK A CHORD IN ARCEUS'S HEART.

...BECAUSE YOU WERE DARING ENOUGH TO TRY AND CAPTURE ARCEUS.

137

138

ZWOOOP

ACTLY
AT HE
SAID.

WHAT'S
HE
TALKING
ABOUT
?!

"CRE-
ATION"
?!

146

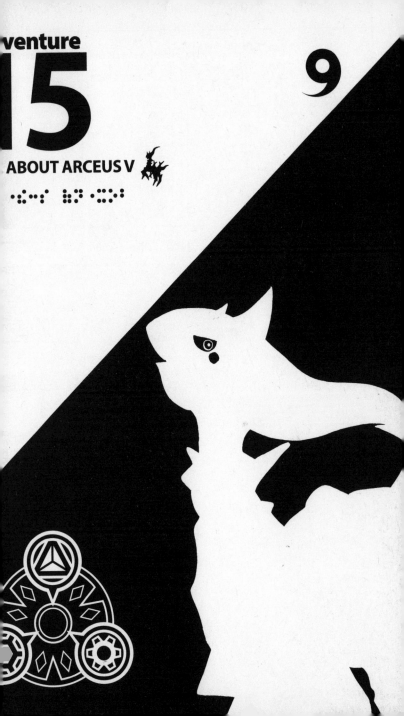

THEY'RE RETURNING TO ARCEUS!

THE PLATES ARE FLYING THROUGH THE AIR TOWARDS...

GOLD?

WHA HAP PENI CRY:

OH ....!

THAT'S WHY I TOLD SILVER TO GO AHEAD AND HAND OVER THE PLATES.

EVEN IF THE ENEMY GOT THEIR CLUTCHES ON THEM, I KNEW THE PLATES WOULD RETURN TO THEIR RIGHTFUL OWNER AS SOON AS ARCEUS APPEARED...

I E PEC' TH

ZIPZIP

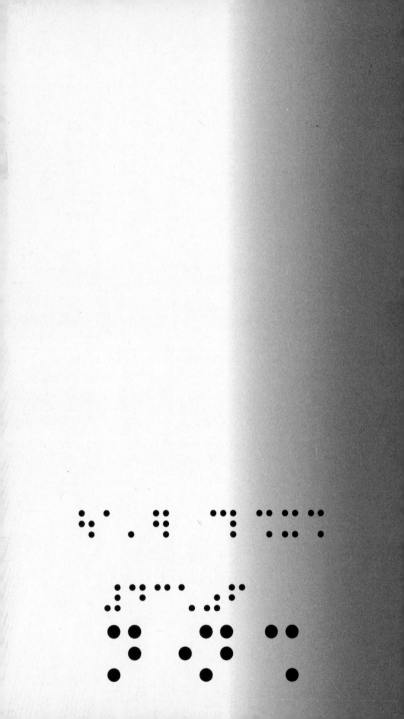

THE ORIGIN OF THE POKÉATHLON

THERE IS A FAMOUS LEGEND BEHIND THE CREATION OF THIS SPORT IN WHICH TRAINERS AND POKÉMON MUST WORK TOGETHER.

BASEMENT MUSEUM: SOLIDARITY ROOM

REACH THE MUSEUM BY TURNING RIGHT AFTER ENTERING THE POKÉATHLON DOME AND TAKING THE ESCALATOR BEHIND THE FRONT DESK DOWN TO THE BASEMENT. THERE ARE SEVERAL ROOMS THERE DEDICATED TO CELEBRATING POKÉATHLETES AND POKÉMON WITH RECORD-BREAKING WINS. WE HAVE GATHERED INFORMATION ON THE FIRST ROOM, THE SOLIDARITY ROOM, FOR THIS ARTICLE.

1 THE OUTBREAK OF AN EPIDEMIC

A TERRIFYING EPIDEMIC THAT NO ONE HAS EXPERIENCED BEFORE IS AT THE ROOT. ITS

AN OLD SCROLL IS ON DISPLAY IN THE SOLIDARITY ROOM. LET'S TAKE A LOOK AT THE HISTORY RECORDED ON IT. INSCRIBED ON THE SCROLL IS THE STORY BEHIND THE ORIGIN OF THE POKÉATHLON. IT'S UNCLEAR WHERE THIS STORY TOOK PLACE. REGARDLESS, A LONG TIME AGO, A DEADLY EPIDEMIC BROKE OUT ON A CERTAIN ISLAND IN A CERTAIN REGION. THE ISLANDERS WERE FILLED WITH DESPAIR AS THEIR PEOPLE COLLAPSED ONE AFTER THE OTHER. THEY HAD NO WAY OF CURING THIS MYSTERIOUS ILLNESS.

2 THE JOURNEY TO FIND THE LEGENDARY POKÉMON IN SEARCH OF A CURE

THE LEGENDARY POKÉMON COULD CURE THE PLAGUE. BUT FINDING IT WOULDN'T BE EASY!

ONE TRAINER SEARCHED FOR HELP. AFTER HEARING THAT A LEGENDARY POKÉMON MIGHT BE ABLE TO CURE THIS PLAGUE, THE TRAINER SET OUT ON A JOURNEY WITH THREE POKÉMON TO FIND THIS LEGENDARY POKÉMON.

POKÉATHLON OWNER

MAGNUS

THE TRAINER AND THE POKÉMON WORKED TOGETHER AND DIDN'T GIVE UP. FINALLY, THEY REACHED THE LEGENDARY POKÉMON.

THE TRAINER ENCOUNTERED MANY OBSTACLES ALONG THE WAY, CHALLENGES THAT COULD NOT BE OVERCOME BY JUST THE TRAINER OR THE POKÉMON ALONE!

3. OVERCOMING THE TEN ORDEALS AND MEETING THE LEGENDARY POKÉMON

THE TRAINER AND THE POKÉMON MET THE LEGENDARY POKÉMON AND RECEIVED THE CURE. THE STORY OF THEIR FRIENDSHIP WAS PASSED DOWN FOR GENERATIONS. EVENTUALLY, THE SURVIVORS OF THE PLAGUE MEMORIALIZED THIS EVENT BY CREATING TEN CHALLENGING SPORTS INSPIRED BY THE TEN ORDEALS!

4. THE CREATION OF TEN SPORTS THAT REPLICATE THOSE ORDEALS

THE MURAL IN THE MUSEUM DEPICTS A TRAINER AND THREE POKÉMON RECEIVING SOMETHING FROM A POKÉMON IN THE SKY. ONE THEORY HAS IT THAT THIS MYSTERIOUS POKÉMON IS CELEBI. IS IT CORRECT?

JOHTO REGION'S LEGENDARY POKÉMON

CELEBI

- HEIGHT: 2' 00"
- WEIGHT: 11.0 LBS.
- CATEGORY: TIME TRAVEL POKÉMON
- GENDER: UNKNOWN
- TYPE: PSYCHIC / GRASS
- ABILITY: NATURAL CURE
- POKÉDEX NUMBER: JOHTO POKÉDEX: 256. NATIONAL POKÉDEX: 251.

▲ A LEGENDARY POKÉMON SAID TO BE THE HARBINGER OF A BRIGHT FUTURE.

THE POKÉMON ON GOLD'S TEAM

Exbo/Typhlosion ♂

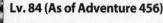

Lv. 84 (As of Adventure 456)

Ability: Blaze

Impish Nature. A little quick-tempered.

main attacker on Gold's team. It can use powerful moves, including a special ype move. It can also carry Gold on its back.

Aibo/Ambipom ♂

Lv. 83 (As of Adventure 456)

Ability: Technician

Naive Nature. Mischievous.

Aibo has known Gold since he was a baby, is like a family member. Aibo uses its fight in tricky ways.

Polibo/Politoed ♂

Lv. 80 (As of Adventure 456)

Ability: Water Absorb

Quiet Nature. Capable of absorbing attacks.

nily member like Aibo, who evolved g a trade with Silver. Uses Fighting- and r-type moves.

● Subo/Sudowoodo

`ROCK`

- Lv. 78 (As of Adventure 456)
- Ability: Sturdy
- Jolly Nature. Often scatters things.

It joined the team after taking a liking to Gold. In the beginning, Subo was rather timid, but its courage grew after experiencing various battles. Uses its powerful Low Kick in battle.

● Sunbo/Sunflora ♀

`GRASS`

- Lv. 75 (As of Adventure 456)
- Ability: Chlorophyll
- Serious Nature. Finicky.

A serious-minded Pokémon who cannot ignore others in trouble. Fights with Grass-type moves and supports Exbo by using Sunny Day.

● Togebo/Togepi ♂

`NORMAL`

- Lv. 81 (As of Adventure 456)
- Ability: Hustle
- Naughty Nature. Hates to lose.

Born from an egg that Professor Elm entrusted to Gold. It is naughty natured like Gold and has the courage to face even the toughest opponents.

Pibu was born from an egg held by Red's Pika and Yellow's Chuchu. It has a pointy forelock because Gold hatched the egg. Pibu doesn't seem to be one of the six Pokémon who Gold has with him now...

● **Pibu/Pichu** ●

TITLE PAGE ILLUSTRATIONS

PRESENTING TITLE PAGE ILLUSTRATIONS DRAWN FOR SOME OF THE PREVIOUS CHAPTERS UPON FIRST PUBLICATION IN THE JAPANESE CHILDREN'S MAGAZINE *COROCORO ICHIBAN!* STAND-ALONE TITLE PAGES LIKE THESE ARE RARE IN THE HISTORY OF THE POKÉMON ADVENTURES SERIES.

Corocoro Ichiban! July Issue, 2010

Corocoro Ichiban!
September Issue, 2010

Corocoro Ichiban! November Issue, 2010

venture

16

. ABOUT ARCEUS VI

∴∵ ⠢⠇

9

ILEX FOREST...

ME TOO.

THIS FOREST IS LIKE A MAZE TO ME NO MATTER HOW MANY TIMES I'VE BEEN HERE!

BUT I COULDN'T BELIEVE MY EYES!

I KNOW, KEN!

DON'T COMPLAIN! WE'RE ACTING ON DIRECT ORDERS FROM YOU-KNOW-WHO, YOU KNOW!

HARRY...   AL...

RIGHT AFTER APPEARING IN FRONT OF US OUT OF THE BLUE!

HE TOLD US TO GET RID OF ANY SUSPICIOUS LOOKING PEOPLE IN THE ILEX FOREST...

...THIS BATTLE...

...ARE GLARING AT GIRATINA MENACINGLY.

DIALGA AND PALKIA...

...BUT THEY SEEM TO REMEMBER THEIR ANCIENT RIVALRY WELL!

RIGHT! THOSE LEGENDARY POKÉMON HAVE JUST BEEN RECREATED ...

THE TWO OF THEM BANISHED GIRATINA FROM THIS WORLD BECAUSE IT ONCE WREAKED DESTRUCTION UPON IT.

OF COURSE ...

NOW THAT THE THREE OF THEM ARE TOGETHER...

AND GIRATINA IS BRIMMING WITH ANGER OVER ITS LONG-HELD GRUDGE AGAINST THE OTHER TWO.

DIALGA AND PALKIA ARE FILLED WITH SUSPICION OF GIRATINA.

WHAT DO YOU KNOW ABOUT IT?!

YOU TALK AS IF YOU WERE THERE!

...WITHOUT UNDERSTANDING THEIR RELATIONSHIP.

YOU'RE A FOOL TO IMAGINE YOU CAN CONTROL THESE THREE LEGENDARIES ...

I WENT TO SO MUCH TROUBLE TO CREATE THESE LEGENDARY POKÉMON!

B-BUT... GIOVANNI... **WHY?!**

...WILL TAKE CARE OF THE DRAGON THAT CONTROLS ANTI-MATTER.

THE I...

PLEASE DON'T STOP THEM, GIO-VANNI!!

IN OTHER WORDS, WE'RE IN A SPECIAL REALM CONNECTING THE JOHTO REGION AND THE FAR-OFF SINNOH REGION.

THIS PLACE CANNOT BE LOCATED ON ANY MAP. IT'S IN ANOTHER DIMENSION.

WHAT WOULD HAPPEN IF AN ..L-OUT BATTLE BEGAN HERE BETWEEN THESE THREE LEGENDARY DRAGON-TYPE POKÉMON?

IT'S AN EXTREMELY UNSTABLE SPOT.

..TAKING JOHTO AND SINNOH ALONG WITH IT!

THIS REALM WOULD COLLAPSE AND DISINTE- GRATE...

FROM THE CRACK OF TIME... I SAW THE END OF JOHTO AND SINNOH!

...THIS PLACE HAS ALREADY FALLEN APART ONCE.

AS A MATTER OF FACT...

194

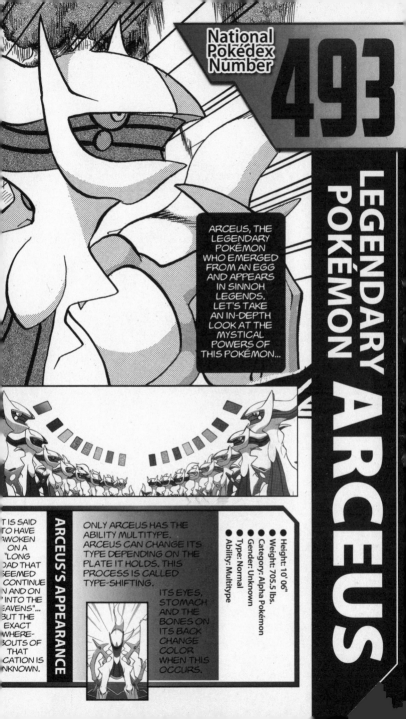

493

LEGENDARY POKÉMON ARCEUS

ARCEUS, THE LEGENDARY POKÉMON WHO EMERGED FROM AN EGG AND APPEARS IN SINNOH LEGENDS. LET'S TAKE AN IN-DEPTH LOOK AT THE MYSTICAL POWERS OF THIS POKÉMON...

ARCEUS'S APPEARANCE

IT IS SAID TO HAVE AWOKEN ON A "LONG ROAD THAT SEEMED TO CONTINUE ON AND ON" INTO THE HEAVENS"... BUT THE EXACT WHERE-ABOUTS OF THAT LOCATION IS UNKNOWN.

ONLY ARCEUS HAS THE ABILITY MULTITYPE. ARCEUS CAN CHANGE ITS TYPE DEPENDING ON THE PLATE IT HOLDS. THIS PROCESS IS CALLED TYPE-SHIFTING.

ITS EYES, STOMACH AND THE BONES ON ITS BACK CHANGE COLOR WHEN THIS OCCURS.

- Height: 10'06"
- Weight: 705.5 lbs.
- Category: Alpha Pokémon
- Gender: Unknown
- Type: Normal
- Ability: Multitype

▲ THE SIXTEEN PLATES ALL HAVE SOMETHING ABOUT ARCEUS WRITTEN ON THEM.

IF A POKÉMON OTHER THAN ARCEUS HOLDS A PLATE OF A CERTAIN TYPE, IT WILL BOOST THE POWER OF ANY OF ITS MOVES OF THAT TYPE.

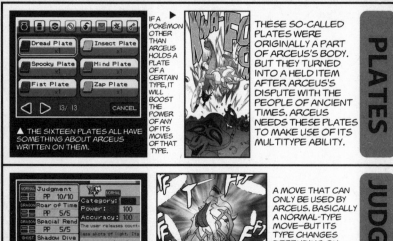

THESE SO-CALLED PLATES WERE ORIGINALLY A PART OF ARCEUS'S BODY. BUT THEY TURNED INTO A HELD ITEM AFTER ARCEUS'S DISPUTE WITH THE PEOPLE OF ANCIENT TIMES. ARCEUS NEEDS THESE PLATES TO MAKE USE OF ITS MULTITYPE ABILITY.

▲ THE USER RELEASES COUNTLESS SHOTS OF LIGHT. ITS TYPE VARIES DEPENDING UPON THE KIND OF PLATE THE USER IS HOLDING.

▲ IT CAN CHANGE TO ANY TYPE OF MOVE, DEPENDING ON THE PLATE IT HOLDS. THIS ATTACK SUITS A POKÉMON WHO CREATED ALL THINGS!

A MOVE THAT CAN ONLY BE USED BY ARCEUS. BASICALLY A NORMAL-TYPE MOVE—BUT ITS TYPE CHANGES DEPENDING ON THE PLATE ARCEUS IS HOLDING. THIS ATTACK STRIKES AN OPPONENT WITH SHOTS OF LIGHT ENERGY.

▲ A RUIN WITH ANCIENT POWERS. THE JOHTO SIDE ENTRANCE WAS FOUND AT THE RUINS OF ALPH.

▲ YOU CAN ONLY ENTER IT TOGETHER WITH ARCEUS.

THE RUIN WITH THE MYSTRI STAGE WHERE ARCEUS PERFORMED ITS CREATION. THE SINJOH RUINS ARE CONNECTED TO THE RUINS OF ALPH, BUT EXIST IN A REALM THAT IS NEITHER SINNOH NOR JOHTO.

▲ A HORDE OF UNOWN FLYING IN THE AIR... THE MOMENT THE LEGENDARY DRAGONS WERE CREATED.

THESE THREE POKÉMON ARE SAID TO HAVE BEEN CREATED BY ARCEUS WHEN IT CREATED THE WORLD.

UPON GETTING THE PLATES BACK, ARCEUS MATERIALIZED DIALGA, PALKIA AND GIRATINA. THIS IS WHY ARCEUS IS CALLED THE ALPHA POKÉMON.

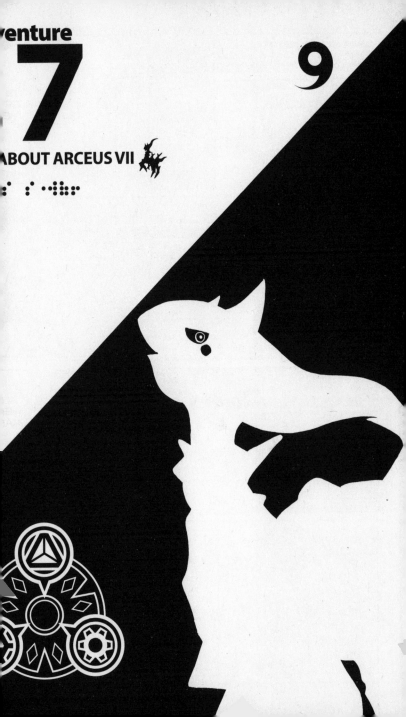

208

...ARE THE KIND OF PEOPLE YOU'D LIKE TO TURN YOUR BACK ON.

I'M SURE THOSE BAD GUYS AND ME...

HEY, ARCEUS!

DON'T GO TO THE EXTREME OF WIPING ALL OF US OUT!

CAN'T YOU AT LEAST RESTORE YOUR FAITH IN US BECAUSE OF CRYS? SHE'S A PERSON!

IS THAT BECAUSE YOU THOUGHT YOU COULD MAYBE TRUST HER?

BUT I HEARD THAT YOU LET CRYS CAPTURE YOU FOR A SECOND.

BUT NOW HE SAYS HIS MISSION IS TO SAVE THE WORLD!

OLD MAN PRYCE USED TO SAY EVERYONE WAS EXPENDABLE— EXCEPT HIS POKÉMON.

LANCE! SILVER'S FATHER IS...

FATHER!!

THEN I HAVE NO REGRETS... ...EVEN IF I DIE HERE...

HUE HUE HUE

SO THAT'S THE REASON HE'S BEEN SEARCHING FOR CELEBI.

IT'S JUST LIKE THE STORY FROM THE HISTORY OF THE POKÉATHLON!

HE WANTED TO MEET CELEBI TO GET THE CURE FOR HIS ILLNESS...

DOES HE MEAN... PIBU?!

!! GOLD'S POKÉMON IS HELPING CELEBI TOO.

AND AS WE SPEAK, CELEBI IS GATHERING THE INGREDIENTS FOR HIS MEDICINE IN THE ILEX FOREST.

218

222

223

...HELP ARCEUS...

W
CA

FW

ITS SKILLS ARE TOP-NOTCH!

THAT'S TRUE! BUT I...

HA HA HA... WELL, OF COURSE! I'VE KNOWN TOGEBO SINCE IT WAS STILL AN EGG!!

THAT WAS *AMAZING!* IT'S AS IF YOU TWO HAVE A SYMBIOTIC UNDER-STANDING OF EACH OTHER!!

AND THEY KIND OF LOOK LIKE EACH OTHER TOO! *TEE HEE...*

231

venture

19

9

ABOUT ARCEUS IX

∴∷ ∙∴∵

235

236

...BEFORE THERE WAS A UNIVERSE.

THE ORIGINAL ONE BREATHED ALONE.

...AND THREE MAKE SPIRIT...

TWO MAKE MATTER...

TWO BEINGS OF TIME AND SPACE...SET FREE FROM THE ORIGINAL ONE.

AND THE RIGHTFUL BEARER OF A PLATE DRAWS POWER FROM IT.

THE POWERS OF THE PLATES ARE SHARED BETWEEN ALL POKÉMON.

AND WHEN THE UNIVERSE WAS CREATED, ITS SHARDS BECAME THESE PLATES.

...THE WORLD.

...THEREBY SHAPING...

242

YOU DIDN'T TURN TO EVIL BECAUSE SILVER WAS KIDNAPPED?

YOU MEAN...

I ERADICATED ANY GOOD INSIDE ME WHEN I DECIDED TO PURSUE THE PATH TO ABSOLUTE POWER.

ARE YOU JOKING?

HUF.

HUF.

AND YOU'VE GOT A FEMALE PICHU WITH YOU!

HEY, PIBU! I DIDN'T KNOW YOU WERE HERE...

WE'VE BROUGHT CELEBI'S MEDICINE!!

THE MEDICINE!!

GIOVANNI!!

WE FINALLY MANAGED TO FULFILL OUR MISSION!

...OVANNI!! OH!!

244

248

...ALREADY ACCEPT US FROM THE START!

MAYBE ARCEUS DID...

HEY, TOGEBO!

FOR SOME REASON, THAT'S THE SENSE I GOT...

254

HA! IT'S ABOUT A TRANS-FORMING ROBOT!

WHAT THE—?

CHILDREN'S ROBOT SHOW
Proteam Omega

Top Secret

WHAT THE...?

PROJECT PROPOSAL

SNOR
MEGA RESCUE

THIS IS...

AERO
(MEGA BALLOON)

GYARA
(OMEGA SHIP)

HEY!

POLI
MEGA TRAIN

PIKA
(OMEGA PLANE)

HEY...

COMMANDER SAUR

I GOT SUCH A KICK OUT OF WATCHING HIM TRAIN HIS POKÉMON ON MT. SILVER!

THESE ARE A TOTAL RIP-OFF OF RED'S POKÉMON!!

OH. CAN YOU TELL?

258

259

AND
...

Has he gained weight?

More presents from his groupies?

Suicur

THE DAYS PASS UNTIL ...

Uh-huh...

You want ten of these capes?

PROTS HEX

Hey! Are you going to camp out at my house until the show starts?!

261

262

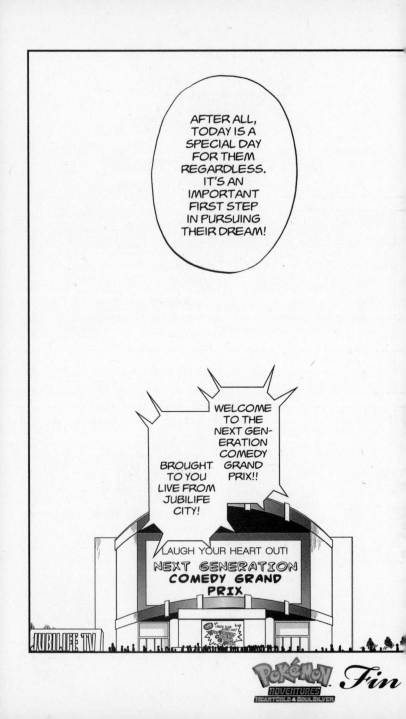

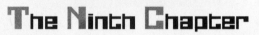

The Ninth Chapter

HEARTGOLD & SOULSILVER
Secret Japanese-Braille Chapter Titles Decoded!

GO TO THE NEXT Chapter!!

Message from
Hidenori Kusaka

I had a very hard time figuring out how one could defeat Arceus in the Ninth Chapter story arc because "It can change itself to any Pokémon type..." "It's an Alpha Pokémon..." Hm... The more I thought about it, the harder it seemed. But after a while, I became interested in Arceus's perspective. So I asked the same question as Gold. "Arceus! Tell me more about yourself!!" What would Arceus's answer be? You'll find out in this volume!!

Message from
Satoshi Yamamoto

One word to describe the HeartGold SoulSilver story arc is "reassemble." Gold, Silver and Crystal have been on their own, but now they have reassembled. The Plates have been reassembled too, and thus Arceus can transform into seventeen different types (including the Normal type). And in this volume you will witness an even more surprising "reassemblage"... Enjoy this story of "reassemblies"!

The adventure continues in the Johto region!

POKÉMON™
ADVENTURES
GOLD & SILVER BOX SET

Includes
POKÉMON
ADVENTURES
Vols. 8-14
and a collectible
poster!

Story by
HIDENORI KUSAKA

Art by
MATO,
SATOSHI YAMAMOTO

More exciting Pokémon adventures starring Gold and his rival Silver! First someone steals Gold's backpack full of Poké Balls (and Pokémon!). Then someone steals Prof. Elm's Totodile. Can Gold catch the thief—or thieves?!

Keep an eye on Team Rocket, Gold... Could they be behind this crime wave

POKÉMON™

SUN & MOON

Story
Hidenori Kusaka

Art
Satoshi Yam

Sun dreams of money. Moon dreams
scientific discoveries. When their paths
with Team Skull, both their plans go aw

**PICK UP YOUR COPY AT YOUR
LOCAL BOOK STORE.**

READ THIS WAY

THIS IS THE END OF THIS GRAPHIC NOVEL!

properly enjoy this VIZ Media aphic novel, please turn it around d begin reading from right to left.

is book has been printed in the iginal Japanese format in order preserve the orientation of the iginal artwork.

ve fun with it!

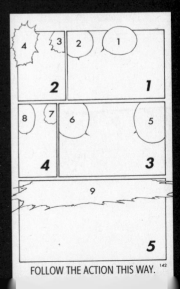

FOLLOW THE ACTION THIS WAY.